Illustrated
Stories *from the* Bible

Volume 8

AUTHORS
George and Marilyn Durrant
Former Professor of Ancient Scriptures

Doctor of Education

ARTIST AND ART DIRECTOR
Vernon Murdock
Artist Illustrator

Bachelor of Fine Arts
Graduate Work, University of Madrid,
    Spain

CORRELATORS AND DIRECTORS
Steven R. Shallenberger, *President*
Community Press, Wisdom House, Eagle
    Marketing Corporation

Bachelor of Science; Accounting, Business.
SCMP, Graduate School of Business, Harvard
    University

Paul R. Cheesman
Director of Scripture in Religious Study Center
Chaplain, U.S. Navy

Doctor of Religious Education

Lael J. Woodbury
Chairman, National Committee on Royalties,
    American Theatre Association

Doctor of Philosophy, University of Illinois

ADVISORS
Dale T. Tingey
Director of American Indian Services and
    Research Center

Doctor of Philosophy, Guidance and
    Counseling; Washington State University

Reverend Raymond E. Ansel
Ordained Minister

Southwestern Assemblies of God College, Texas
Berean Bible School, Missouri

Millie Foster Cheesman
Writer, Poetess

M.J. Bardon
Missionary-Pastor, Grace Baptist Church

Th. M. Clarksville School of Theology
    Clarksville, Tennessee

Reverend William R. Schroeder
United Church of Christ

United Theological Seminary of the Twin Cities
    New Brighton, Minnesota

Copyright © 1980 by
EAGLE SYSTEMS INTERNATIONAL
Library of Congress Catalog Card No.: 80-80314
ISBN: 0-911712-68-2

FIRST EDITION VOLUME 8, 1981
First Printing March 1982

Lithographed in U.S.A.
by
COMMUNITY PRESS, INC.
P.O. Box 1229
Antioch, California 94509

A Member of
The American Bookseller's Association
New York, New York

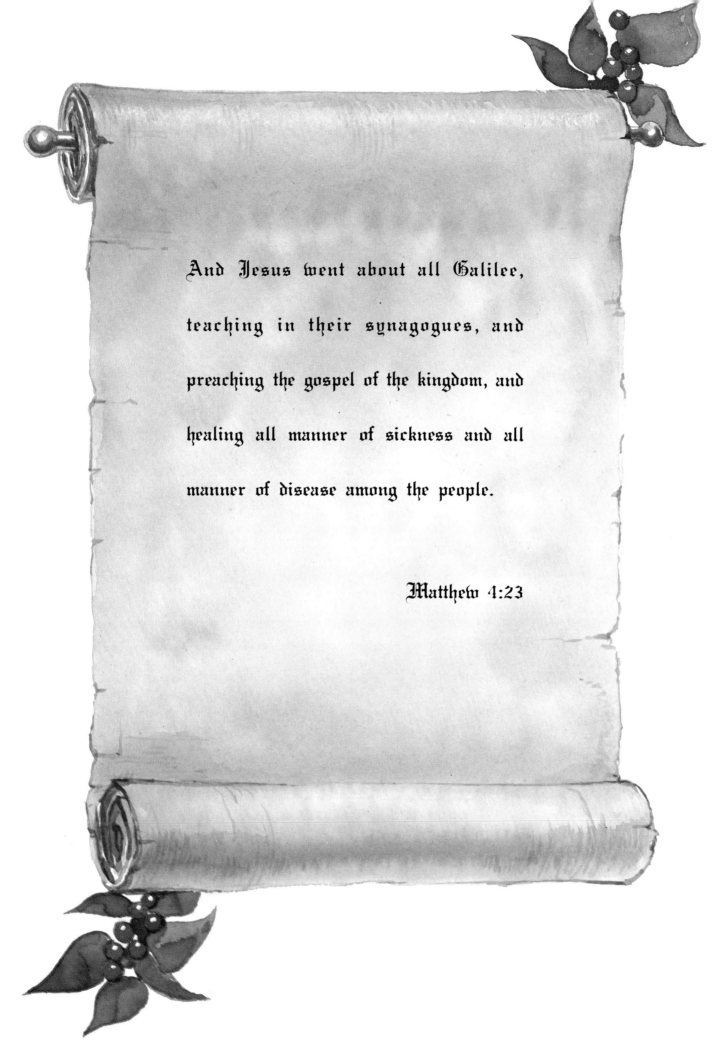

And Jesus went about all Galilee,

teaching in their synagogues, and

preaching the gospel of the kingdom, and

healing all manner of sickness and all

manner of disease among the people.

Matthew 4:23

Dedicated to boys and girls throughout the world and to all who love the Bible.

A nondenominational work.

CONTENTS

Our story so far.. 7

Live Up to Your Name *(John the Baptist)* 9

Follow Jesus *(The First Disciples)* 14

The Greatest Message *(Nicodemus)* 18

A Message for All *(The Samaritan Woman)* 22

Fishers of Men *(Peter, James, and John)* 28

A Blessing for All *(The Work in Galilee)* 36

The Way To Be Blessed *(The Beatitudes)* 42

Be Ye Therefore Perfect *(Sermon on the Mount)* 50

The Miracles of Jesus *(Water into Wine)* 64

Power over Death *(The Nobleman's Son)* 70

Raised from the Dead *(The Widow's Son)* 74

She Shall Live *(Jairus' Daughter)* 79

A Great Calm in Our Hearts *(Calming the Storm)* 82

Trouble Begins *(The Jewish Leaders)* 87

Preparing for the Future *(Calling and Training the Twelve)* 95

Go in Peace *(Faith Makes a Sick Woman Whole)* 100

Finding One's Life *(The Twelve Go on a Mission)* 105

The Most Important Food *(Feeding the Five Thousand)* 110

Go and Sin No More *(Jesus Helps Sinners)* 117

Helping Us Understand *(Teaching Through Parables)* 122

Nourish the Good Seeds *(The Parable of the Sower)* 127

Preview of Volume Nine 135

Our story so far . . .

Since the time of Adam and Eve, prophets and righteous people had looked forward to the time when the promised Messiah would come. Finally the long-awaited time arrived. On a quiet night in Bethlehem, Jesus Christ, the Savior of the world, was born in a stable. Angels sang and told shepherds of the glorious event. Wise men came to see the Christchild.

Jesus grew into manhood and was ready to begin his ministry. In the last volume we read of Jesus' baptism by John the Baptist. After this he was tempted by Satan but remained faithful to his divine mission.

In Volume Eight we will read how Jesus calls others to help him in his work. He will teach the people through parables, perform miracles, and show us what it means to truly love one another.

LIVE UP TO YOUR NAME
John the Baptist

John was called "the Baptist" because he baptized many people—including Jesus. But this great prophet could well have been called "John the Helper" because it was his purpose to help Jesus by preparing the people for the message he would bring.

John might well have been called "John the Humble" because he never sought after fame and glory for himself. When speaking to a group of people who loved him, John told them that Jesus was much greater than he was. He said, "[Jesus'] shoe's latchet [lace] I am not worthy to unloose." (John 1:27)

He could have been called "John the Teacher," for he taught people to follow Jesus. While speaking to friends, he said, pointing to Jesus at a distance, "Behold the Lamb of God! And the two disciples heard him speak, and they followed Jesus." (John 1:36, 37)

He could have been called "John the Unselfish" because he was willing to work for someone else's glory and he was never jealous of Jesus. He spoke boldly to his friends, saying, "He must increase, but I *must* decrease." (John 3:30) Then he added with warmth, "The Father loveth the Son, and hath given all things into his hand." (John 3:35)

He could have been called "John the Brave," for he was not afraid to say what he knew he should, even if he should lose his own life for saying it. He taught the truth with power. Some loved his message, did as he asked, and followed Jesus. Others, who were wicked in their hearts and in their deeds, hated John and planned for the day when they could kill him.

Yes, this mighty prophet who loved and taught in the wilderness could have been known by many names. Yet today he is known in the world as John the Baptist, and he is appreciated for his service of teaching others to follow Jesus.

THINK ABOUT IT

1. If you could rename John the Baptist, what would you name him? Why?
2. If you could have a name like John the Baptist, what would you like it to be? Use your first name in the first blank: _____ the _____ .

FOLLOW JESUS
The First Disciples

One of John's followers was a man named Andrew. After talking to Jesus one day, Andrew went to the home of his brother, Peter, and with great excitement shouted, "Peter, we have found him. We have found the Messiah!" Peter quickly ran to see for himself if Jesus really was who he claimed to be.

Peter was not disappointed when he met Jesus. Something in his heart told him that this was indeed the Son of God.

The next day as Jesus was walking along a narrow path, he saw a man nearby named Philip. Speaking to him, he said, "Follow me." Philip followed Jesus and later hurried off to find his best friend, whose name was Nathanael. With deep emotion Philip said, "We have found him, of whom Moses in the law, and the prophets, did write, Jesus of Nazareth. . . ." (John 1:45)

Nathanael and Philip returned together to see the Savior. As Jesus saw the men approaching, he spoke to a disciple nearby, saying: "Here comes a man in whom there is no guile." Somehow Nathanael's eyes and spirit radiated in such a way that Jesus could tell Nathanael had only good feelings in his heart. Andrew, Peter, Philip, Nathanael, and many more men and women who wanted to be honest and good learned about Jesus. They all became his disciples (followers).

THINK ABOUT IT

1. If your friend said to you, "We have found the Messiah," would you be willing to leave some part of your life behind and follow him? Why?
2. If Jesus saw you coming toward him, could he look into your eyes and say of you, "Here comes a person in whom there are no bad feelings"? How could you help this to happen?

THE GREATEST MESSAGE
Nicodemus

Peter, Nathanael, and others who followed Jesus were excited about the things that he taught them and they told others. Among those who heard about Jesus was a man named Nicodemus. This man felt that the words he had heard were true, and he believed that Jesus was the Son of God. To himself Nicodemus thought, "But how could I follow Jesus? I am a leader of the Jewish people. If my friends and the other leaders found out that I was a follower of this humble man from Nazareth, they would laugh at me and I would be forced to give up all that I have."

The more Nicodemus thought about it, the more he worried. Finally, one dark night he said, "I can stand it no longer. I must see him." Secretly leaving his home, he made his way to where Jesus was. He felt more comfortable when Jesus greeted him warmly, and mustering all his courage, Nicodemus spoke, "Rabbi, we know that thou art a teacher come from God: for no man can do these miracles that thou doest, except God be with him." (John 3:2)

Jesus sensed that Nicodemus wanted to follow him, but he could also tell that he was fearful to do so because of what people would say. Speaking to Nicodemus, Jesus said, ". . . Except a man be born of water and *of* the Spirit, he cannot enter into the kingdom of God." (John 3:5) Nicodemus knew that Jesus was telling him to follow him and that by doing so he could become part of the kingdom of God. Still Nicodemus hesitated.

Knowing the thoughts that were in the heart of this good but fearful man, Jesus then spoke a message that all people in the world will someday hear. He said softly but powerfully,

> For God so loved the world, that he gave his only begotten Son, that whosoever believeth in him should not perish, but have everlasting life.
>
> John 3:16

A MESSAGE FOR ALL
The Samaritan Woman

The disciples often grew tired as they walked from village to village with Jesus. One night as they were lying down to sleep, one said to another, "The leader Nicodemus was taught well by the master." "Yes," agreed the other. "Perhaps it was to meet him that we walked these many long miles to Jerusalem." "Perhaps," said the other, "but in the morning we start the weary walk home. It wouldn't be so bad except that tomorrow we will be in Samaria, and you know how the Samaritans hate us Jews." "And we hate them," said the other.

Morning came and Jesus and his followers traveled north. Soon they were in the land of Samaria. All day as they walked along the hot, dusty roads, the Samaritans whom they passed looked at them with hatred and suspicion. Finally the sun in the western sky was about to disappear.

Tired and hungry, Jesus and his followers made camp near a well. While Jesus remained there, the disciples went into a nearby city to purchase food. As Jesus waited,

There cometh a woman of Samaria to draw water: Jesus saith unto her, Give me to drink.

Then saith the woman of Samaria unto him, How is it that thou, being a Jew, askest drink of me, which am a woman of Samaria? for the Jews have no dealings with the Samaritans.

John 4:7, 9

Jesus was not upset at the woman's words. With a smile he walked nearer to her and said in a soft, clear voice,

Whosoever drinketh of this water shall thirst again:

But whosoever drinketh of the water that I shall give him shall never thirst; but the water that I shall give him shall be in him a well of water springing up into everlasting life.

John 4:13, 14

The woman sensed that this stranger was different than anyone she had ever met before. She wondered if he were the one whom the prophets had promised would come. Finally, she spoke again, "I know that Messias cometh, which is called Christ. . . ." Jesus then said, "I that speak unto thee am *he*." (John 4:25, 26)

Hurrying back to the city, the Samaritan woman told her family and friends what had happened. Some didn't believe her, but others were not sure, so they went out to the well themselves and were taught by Jesus. As Jesus spoke to them, they knew that the woman was right.

And many more believed because of his own word;

And [they] said unto the woman, Now we believe, not because of thy saying: for we have heard *him* ourselves, and know that this is indeed the Christ, the Saviour of the world.

John 4:41, 42

FISHERS OF MEN
Peter, James, and John

Sometime later, after Jesus and his followers had left Samaria and were just a few miles from Nazareth, one of the disciples said to another, "I'm glad we will soon be in Nazareth, where Jesus grew up. If the Samaritans believed him, it should be even easier to persuade the people in his own city to follow him." The other nodded in agreement.

These disciples were soon to discover they were wrong. After eating and resting, Jesus went to the local Jewish synagogue. There he told the leaders and other listeners many of the same things that he had told the Samaritans.

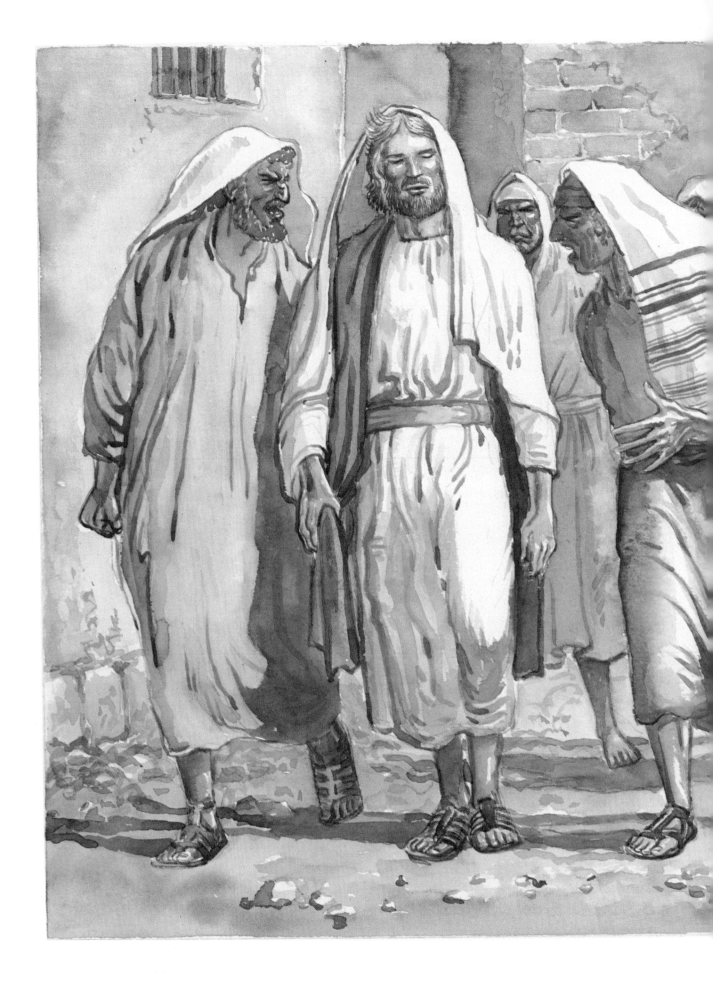

But the same message that had made his so-called enemies of Samaria want to do good now made his supposed friends in his hometown angry and jealous. One said, "Who does he think he is, trying to teach us? We should be teaching him." Another shouted, "This man has no right to teach us. Let us cast him out of our synagogue and out of our city." Others joined in the shouts of hatred. Two men grabbed the arms of Jesus and, with the mob following, took him to the edge of the city. Then an angry leader shouted, "Let's take him to the top of that hill and cast him headlong onto the rocks below!"

Then a marvelous thing happened. One of those who had been holding Jesus shouted, "Where did he go?" Others looked around in astonishment. Somehow Jesus had quietly turned and, ". . . passing through the midst of them went his way." (Luke 4:30)

That must have been a sad day for Jesus, for he had grown up with these people and he loved them. He wanted all of them to have eternal life, but now many of them were rejecting him.

Jesus then journeyed several miles to the shores of the Sea of Galilee. Standing on the bank, he saw a boat bobbing up and down in the water. In the boat were two men:

. . . Simon called Peter, and Andrew his brother, casting a net into the sea: for they were fishers.
And he saith unto them, Follow me, and I will make you fishers of men.
And they straightway left *their* nets, and followed him.

And going on from thence, he saw other two brethren, James *the son* of Zebedee, and John his brother, in a ship with Zebedee their father, mending their nets; and he called them.

And they immediately left the ship and their father, and followed him.

Matthew 4:18-22

As Jesus often did, he was teaching these men a concept by comparing something that wasn't well-known with something that was. These four good men, who later became apostles, knew what it meant to catch fish in a net. When Jesus used this idea as an example, they knew that he was asking them to come and assist him in casting forth the gospel net in order that men, women, and children everywhere might have everlasting life.

When the people of Nazareth rejected Jesus, Satan must have rejoiced; but he also must have been disappointed when these four men decided to help Jesus in his work.

THINK ABOUT IT

When Jesus said, "I will make you fishers of men," what do you think he meant?

A BLESSING FOR ALL
The Work in Galilee

Time passed. Although many rejected Jesus, many others followed and loved him. Each day he would arise early and, after eating, would teach in a little town or village. After each group had received his message, he would move on to another place. He wanted everyone to hear the words of eternal life. Before long there was a crowd of people following Jesus from place to place. These people wanted to be with him day and night.

37

One morning, in order to have time to be alone and pray, Jesus arose from his bed before daylight. While the others were still asleep, he quietly slipped away to a place where he was alone. There he talked with his Father in heaven.

At daybreak, when the others awoke, one man asked, "Where is Jesus?" Another answered, "He is not here. Let us search for him." Simon Peter led the way and they soon found Jesus.

And when they had found him, they said unto him, All *men* seek for thee.

And he said unto them, Let us go into the next towns, that I may preach there also: for therefore came I forth.

And he preached in their synagogues throughout all Galilee, and cast out devils.

Mark 1:37-39

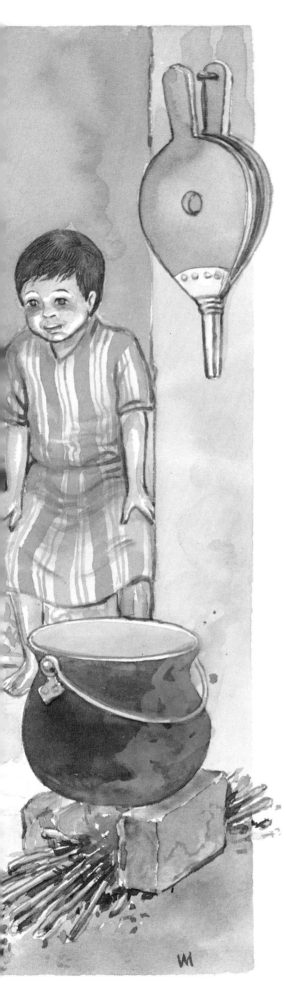

Jesus' fame for healing the sick was also spreading rapidly. Everywhere people were talking about these miracles. One young boy spoke to his mother excitedly, "Mother, we were in the marketplace and heard a man say that he had taken his sick little boy to a man called Jesus. After Jesus had prayed for him, he wasn't sick anymore." The mother responded, "Yes, it's true, my son. Everyone knows about Jesus. Some of the leaders don't like him because they're jealous. But your father and I have heard him speak and we know that he is truly the Son of God."

Thus the fame of Jesus spread throughout the land. People could be seen traveling along almost every road and, when asked where they were going, the answer was always the same, "We are going to find Jesus."

THINK ABOUT IT

The people in the Bible searched for Jesus in their day. How can we search for and find him today?

THE WAY TO BE BLESSED
The Beatitudes

The crowds of people that came to be blessed, healed, and taught by Jesus were continually growing larger. Soon the number of people had grown so great that many could not get close enough to Jesus to see him. Because of his love for each one, Jesus asked them to follow him to a mountainside. As he stood on a high place where all could see him, he motioned for them to be seated.

Those who sat on the mountainside that day were most fortunate, for this was the day that Jesus taught what has become known as the Sermon on the Mount.

Jesus began in a simple manner by telling the people that they would be blessed and happy if they would think, feel, and do certain things.

As all listened, Jesus said, "Blessed *are* the poor in spirit: for theirs is the kingdom of heaven." (Matthew 5:3) When a small girl asked her mother what that meant, her mother replied, "He means that we are all weak and need his help, so we must call upon God in prayer and then he will bless us. If we follow Jesus, someday we will be in the kingdom of heaven with our Heavenly Father."

Next Jesus said, "Blessed *are* they that mourn: for they shall be comforted." (Matthew 5:4) Many of those listening were feeling sad about their past mistakes. Jesus was telling them that if they would follow him, he would teach them how their sins could be forgiven, and they would not need to suffer anymore.

Jesus continued, "Blessed *are* the meek: for they shall inherit the earth." (Matthew 5:5) A young man asked his father, "Does meek mean to be weak?" "Oh no!" replied the father. "Meek people are not weak. To be meek means to be wise enough to know that we are nothing without God's help. If we will ask God to help us, then someday, through his help, we will have all things!"

"Blessed *are* they which do hunger and thirst after righteousness: for they shall be filled." (Matthew 5:6) Jesus was promising the people that if they would listen to his words and be hungry and thirsty for the truth, then he would fill them with his spirit and with joy and peace.

Again Jesus spoke, "Blessed *are* the merciful: for they shall obtain mercy." (Matthew 5:7) Many realized from these words that if they would be kind and forgiving to others and follow the ways of Jesus, then God would forgive them of their own sins.

The voice of Jesus spoke again, "Blessed *are* the pure in heart: for they shall see God." (Matthew 5:8) Many of the listeners understood that Jesus was telling them to think pure thoughts and not to find fault with others. If they would do this, someday they would see God and know him.

Next Jesus said, "Blessed *are* the peacemakers: for they shall be called the children of God." (Matthew 5:9) Those listening knew that if they would tell people about Jesus and the peace that comes in following his teachings, then they would be the children of God forever.

After telling his listeners these beautiful truths, the Savior told them that if they would follow him and do these things, they would be blessed. There would be many who would mock them, hate them, and perhaps even harm them, but through all their persecutions, if they did not turn away from him, he and his Father in heaven would bless them forever.

Jesus enjoyed teaching the people to comfort those who were sad, to seek after forgiveness, to have patience toward others, to be clean in their thinking, and to have peace in their hearts. He wanted them to feel the happiness that comes from knowing you have done the right thing.

These important teachings Jesus gave in the Sermon on the Mount have come to be known as the Beatitudes. By striving to follow these righteous principles, people will be blessed with good feelings in their hearts.

BE YE THEREFORE PERFECT
Sermon on the Mount

The voice of Jesus was neither loud nor harsh as he spoke to the crowd, yet each of those who sat on the side of the mountain could hear every word. His message not only touched their ears but their hearts as well.

His voice touched them deeply, as he swept his hand from one side to the other, saying,

Ye [fathers, mothers, and children] are the light of the world. . . .
Let your light so shine before men, that they may see your good works, and glorify your Father which is in heaven.

Matthew 5:14, 16

As Jesus paused, a young boy asked his father, "What does he mean?" His father replied, "He is telling us that those who have found him and have heard his teachings are to be examples. They should try to live in a way that will help others see that they are happier because God is with them."

Jesus reminded the people that for many years they had been taught not to kill. He now told them that they should do even better than that—they shouldn't even get angry with people, especially over things that didn't matter, for anger often led to bloodshed. He taught them not to even think of other sinful acts because he knew that if a person could think a bad thought, it would become easier for him to commit a bad deed.

A woman leaned over and whispered to her husband, "He tells us of the Ten Commandments, but he teaches us a higher law. Not only are we not to do evil, we are not even to think evil thoughts. The law he brings us is a law which we should keep in our hearts." The husband nodded his head in agreement.

Jesus spoke again:

. . . it hath been said, An eye for an eye, and a tooth for a tooth.

Matthew 5:38

The people knew it had long been their practice that if someone did anything against them, they had the right to pay that person back with a punishment equal to his crime.

Jesus continued,

> But I say unto you, That ye resist not evil [with evil]: but whosoever shall smite thee on thy right cheek, turn to him the other also.
>
> Matthew 5:39

The people looked a bit surprised at this statement. Some may have been thinking: "He means that I am not to try to get even with people. Even if a man steals my sheep, I am not to steal his. If someone harms me, I should not feel as though I must harm him in return. Jesus is telling me that I should not let another man's actions affect the way I act myself. I should simply turn my other cheek. What he is teaching me will be difficult to do, but he is right, for I know it is a better way than our old law."

Jesus went on speaking:

And whosoever shall compel
thee to go a mile, go with him twain.

Matthew 5:41

Near the bottom of the mountain some Roman soldiers were passing by. As Jesus looked in the direction of these unpopular men, a man nearby felt Jesus might actually be saying, "If a Roman commands you to carry his bag one mile, you must do it, for he is your master. But if you go a second mile with him, then you are not his slave, but you are your own master.

As Jesus spoke, the children seated around him sensed his love for them. They enjoyed listening to him because he made them feel good inside, and many times they could understand him better than the adults did.

When Jesus spoke again, those who enjoyed being seen giving money to the poor or praying in public bowed their heads slightly. Jesus explained that people should do good deeds, but they should do them secretly so that no one else would know.

If people would do good deeds secretly, their reward wouldn't be measured in praise from those around them but in the happy feelings they would feel in their hearts. Jesus also advised people to pray in secret places, where no one but God could see or hear their prayers.

Then Jesus taught the people to pray by telling them a prayer that should serve as an example of what they might say. In a reverent voice, Jesus said,

After this manner therefore pray ye: Our Father which art in heaven, Hallowed be thy name.

Thy kingdom come. Thy will be done in earth, as *it is* in heaven.

Give us this day our daily bread.

And forgive us our debts, as we forgive our debtors.
And lead us not into temptation, but deliver us from evil: For thine is the kingdom, and the power, and the glory, for ever. Amen.

Matthew 6:9-13

The parents now had an outline to follow in teaching their children to pray. To start with, God should be addressed as "Father." Then, holding God's name as sacred, people should pray for his will to be done on earth. After this they might ask for what they thought they needed, especially for forgiveness of the sins they had committed. Then they might pray for the strength to do what was right, and perhaps they might recognize God's magnificent power. Finally, a prayer should end with an "Amen."

Sometime later Jesus recommended asking for good things in prayers: "Ask, and it shall be given you; seek, and ye shall find; knock, and it shall be opened unto you." (Matthew 7:7)

Jesus mentioned other important truths in the Sermon on the Mount. Among them was a statement that is now called the Golden Rule: "Therefore all things whatsoever ye would that men should do to you, do ye even so to them." (Matthew 7:12) Often it is worded: "Do unto others as you would have others do unto you." Jesus taught that the Golden Rule means we should treat others the way we would like to be treated ourselves. If we do this, our lives will be filled with happiness.

As Jesus often did, he then ended his teaching by telling his listeners a special story or parable. He told them that if people would only do as he taught, they would be like a wise man who built his house upon a rock foundation:

> And the rain descended, and the floods came, and the winds blew, and beat upon that house; and it fell not: for it was founded upon a rock.

> Matthew 7:25

When Jesus had finished speaking, the people began leaving the mountain. A husband reminded his wife as they went along the path: "Remember, he challenged us to be perfect, even as our Father in heaven is perfect."

She replied, "Yes, and with his help, little by little we will succeed. Each day that we teach our children these things, we are building our home on the rock of our Redeemer, which shall never fall."

THINK ABOUT IT

1. Name three things that you have seen people do that look like they are building their homes on sand.
2. Name five things that would help people build their homes on a rock.

THE MIRACLES OF JESUS
Water into Wine

When we read of all that Jesus said and did, we sometimes think that he must have lived and taught for many years. That was not the case. He did almost everything written about him in the Bible in only three years. In order to accomplish so much, he used his time well and saw to it that he completed everything he had been sent to earth to do.

The New Testament tells of many miracles Jesus performed. These miracles were not done just to cause people to believe in him. He did them because he loved people and wanted to help them. His main purpose in performing miracles was to glorify his Father in heaven and to show people the marvelous powers of God. It should always be remembered that it was the ideas Jesus taught and the Holy Spirit that was with him that caused people's hearts to change and made them his true followers.

Miracles may strengthen the faith of those who already believe, but seeing a miracle is soon forgotten if a person doesn't continue to follow the teachings of Jesus.

With this in mind, let us consider some of the miracles Jesus performed during his three year ministry in the Holy Land.

If you have ever been to a party, you know how much everyone enjoys the refreshments. Imagine how disappointing it would be to arrive late to a party and find the refreshments all gone. How embarrassing it would be for the host or hostess who wanted to serve you but couldn't because more people had come than was expected, and all the food had been eaten.

On one occasion Mary, the mother of Jesus, found herself in this difficult situation. While attending a huge wedding feast, Mary noticed that the wine was nearly gone.

As Mary anxiously pondered on how to help, she thought of Jesus. Hurrying to her son, she told him of the problem. As she turned to the servants, she pointed at her son and said,

Whatsoever he saith unto you, do *it*.
And there were set there six waterpots of stone. . . .
Jesus saith unto them, Fill the waterpots with water. And they filled them up to the brim.

And he saith unto them, Draw out now, and bear unto the governor of the feast. And they bare *it*.

When the ruler of the feast had tasted the water that was made wine, . . . [he said] thou hast kept the good wine until now.

John 2:5-10

This was the first recorded miracle that Jesus performed.

POWER OVER DEATH
The Nobleman's Son

Jesus' greatest miracle was to make it possible for all of us to someday rise from the dead and live again. Jesus showed his power over death in other ways. One day as Jesus was returning from a short journey, he saw a man approaching him whose eyes were red from crying. By his appearance Jesus could tell he was a nobleman.

The nobleman begged Jesus, "Please come and heal my son. He is sick and near death." "Then said Jesus unto him, [knowing that miracles do not really change the hearts of the unbelieving,] Except ye see signs and wonders, ye will not believe." (John 4:48) But the nobleman had been sincere in his plea. He believed in Christ and was hardly able to speak because of his sadness. Amidst his tears he pleaded, "Sir, come down ere my child die." (John 4:49) Jesus sensed the nobleman's faith, and he placed his hand on the man's shoulder, saying softly, "Go thy way; thy son liveth." (John 4:50) The nobleman's faith was so strong that he believed every word Jesus had spoken. Thanking Jesus, he turned and hurried toward his home.

Arriving home the next day, the nobleman's servants met him and said, "Thy son liveth." Although the nobleman had already known what they would tell him, still, after being told, his heart overflowed with joy. Embracing the servant who had told him, he asked, "When did he start to get better?" And the servant answered, "Yesterday at the seventh hour the fever left him." (John 4:52) The father realized that this was the exact time Jesus had said to him, "Thy son liveth."

The nobleman's entire household was anxious to hear about his meeting with Jesus. After relating the story to them, he said, "I know in my heart that this man is the Christ, the Son of God." From that time on, everyone in his household believed in Jesus. The miracle had strengthened their faith.

This *is* again the second miracle *that* Jesus did, when he was come out of Judæa into Galilee.

John 4:54

In this miracle Jesus kept death from arriving. In the next miracle death has already come and Jesus restores life once again to one already dead.

RAISED FROM THE DEAD
The Widow's Son

As Jesus approached the gate of the city Nain, he noticed a group of people walking slowly and carrying a young man who had died. Jesus asked, "Who is he?" One of the men answered sadly, "He is the only son of his mother, who is a widow." Following behind was the widow, who was weeping as though her heart would break. By her were many friends trying to comfort her. Feeling deeply sorry for the mother, Jesus said, "Weep not." The woman raised her head, and as she looked at Jesus, a feeling of peace came to her. Jesus walked to the casket where the dead boy lay and spoke in a commanding voice,

Young man, I say unto thee, Arise.
And he that was dead sat up, and began to speak.

Luke 7:14, 15

Reaching out, Jesus took the boy by the hand and led him to his mother. With tears of joy she embraced her son. Those who had witnessed this miracle ". . . glorified God, saying, . . . That God hath visited his people." (Luke 7:16) This rumor that Jesus was God soon spread throughout all Judæa and the region around it.

Besides many who believed, there were some who doubted this miracle, saying it was a trick. No one could bring a dead person back to life. Others thought the boy was merely asleep and later awakened.

SHE SHALL LIVE
Jairus' Daughter

One day a ruler came and bowed before Jesus, saying,

> My daughter is even now dead: but come and lay thy hand upon her, and she shall live [again].

Matthew 9:18

Jesus followed the ruler to his home and saw that the funeral for the young girl had begun. He went to the girl and, touching her forehead, spoke to those around him: ". . . the maid is not dead, but sleepeth." (Matthew 9:24)

Laughter filled the room, as the people mocked Jesus. Someone ordered those who were laughing out of the house. When only a few remained, Jesus took the girl by the hand. Opening her eyes, the young girl sat up.

Those who had been allowed to watch this miracle felt honored. "And the fame hereof went abroad into all that land." (Matthew 9:26)

Although Jesus was becoming famous for his miracles, some of the learned Jews were saying, "His miracles prove nothing. He is a trickster." These jealous Jewish leaders were constantly condemning Jesus. But those who had heard Jesus teach and whose hearts had been touched by the Holy Spirit knew he was the Son of God.

THINK ABOUT IT

1. Why would some leaders say that Jesus was a trickster?
2. How would you try to convince them that he truly was able to perform miracles?

A GREAT CALM IN OUR HEARTS
Calming the Storm

Jesus helped many by healing the sick, bringing hope to those in despair, and by teaching the truth. His followers, wanting to be near him both day and night, followed him everywhere. One of the few ways Jesus could rest was to go out onto the Sea of Galilee in a boat.

One afternoon as the sun was going down, Jesus finished teaching and blessing the people and boarded a nearby ship. With only a few closest friends on board with Jesus, the ship headed into the deep waters of the Sea of Galilee. Before long there arose a violent storm, and as the waves beat against the ship, it began filling with water. Sensing that the ship might soon sink and fearing they all might drown, the disciples searched for Jesus and found him asleep in the back part of the ship.

After a short discussion the disciples hurried to Jesus and, touching his shoulder, one said, "Master, carest thou not that we perish?" (Mark 4:38) Jesus looked up and, seeing fear on his disciples faces, gazed out at the terrible storm. Rebuking the wind and sea, he said, "Peace, be still." To everyone's amazement and joy the wind ceased and there came a great calm. In this sudden silence Jesus patiently spoke again: "Why are ye so fearful? how is it that ye have no faith?" (Mark 4:40)

When Jesus had once again laid down to sleep, the disciples asked one another, "What manner of man is this, that even the wind and the sea obey him?" (Mark 4:41)

Although the storm was over, only Jesus could sleep. The others, watching the stars, wondered: "We have seen him do so much. Surely he must be the Son of God."

All of us must face our own storms in life. These storms are not always made of wind, rain, or snow, but instead they are often storms made by feelings of anger, jealousy, discouragement, or sorrow. Jesus can help calm these storms as well. If we will pray and ask for guidance, we can feel a peace and assurance and will be able to correct what is wrong.

THINK ABOUT IT

1. Name a storm that has been in your heart recently and tell what you did about it.
2. How could Jesus help you calm your storms?

TROUBLE BEGINS
The Jewish Leaders

Some of the Jewish leaders disliked Jesus because many of their followers now followed him. They spoke harshly to anyone who spoke well of Jesus. When one follower was asked why he had been seen with those whom Jesus taught, he replied excitedly, "You should see his miracles. He raises people from the dead, he brings sight to the blind, he gives speech to the dumb, he calms storms. He must be the Son of God!"

"Nonsense," a leader replied with contempt. "He is an imposter and must be destroyed!" Prompted by Satan, he and others secretly began to lay plans to destroy Jesus.

Even with the knowledge that trouble lay ahead, Jesus continued to teach. As the days and weeks passed and the miracles continued, Jesus' fame and following grew. At the same time the Jewish leaders were becoming all the more determined to stop him.

One day a leper (a person with a skin disease that disfigures him and eventually may kill him) came and worshipped Jesus, saying, "Lord, if thou wilt, thou canst make me clean." (Matthew 8:2)

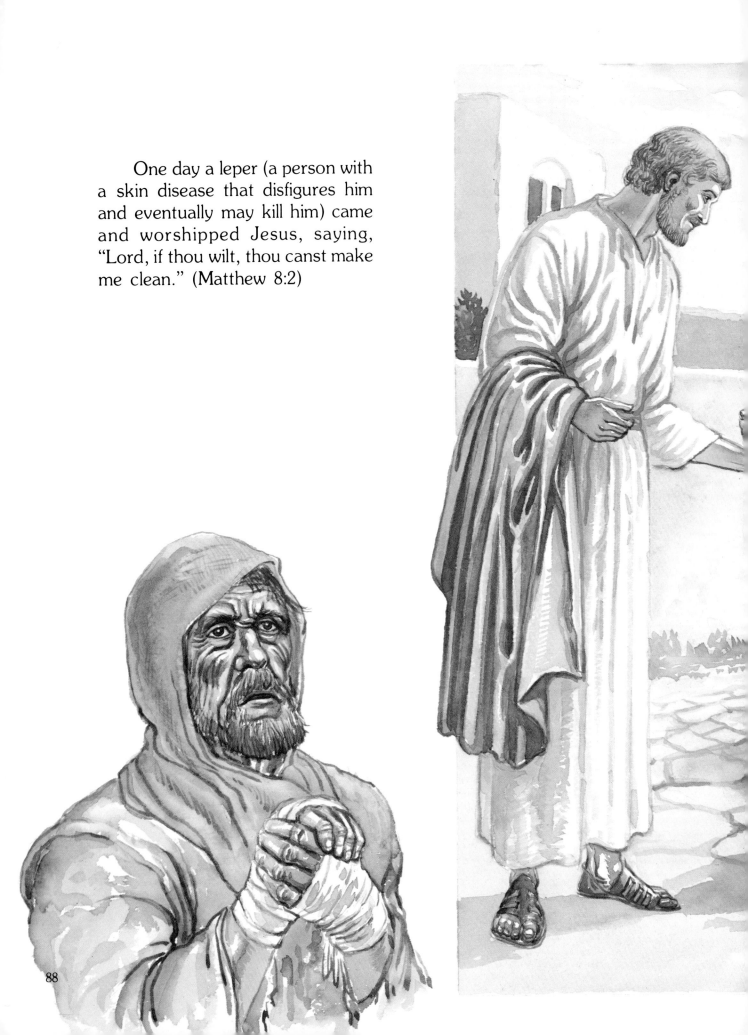

And Jesus put forth *his* hand, and touched him, saying, I will; be thou clean. And immediately his leprosy was cleansed.

And Jesus saith unto him, See thou tell no man; but go thy way. . . .

Matthew 8:3, 4

Jesus knew that the leaders hated him and that if they heard of this miracle, they would be even more determined to put him to death. In spite of this danger, Jesus continued his work.

Jesus went to Capernaum, and soon everybody in the city knew he was there. Large crowds gathered around the building where he was preaching. Because there were so many and there was no room to receive them, Jesus stood by the door and preached to them. In the distance four men came, carrying a sick friend. As they came closer and saw the crowd, one of the men shouted, "Stand aside and let us through. We must get this man to Jesus."

"Take your turn," cried someone from the crowd. "We have been here for hours." There seemed little hope of their getting closer.

"I have an idea," said one of the
men carrying the sick man. "See
that flat roof? We can go around
behind the house, climb up on the
roof, and then lower our friend
down through the hole in the top
into the house!" A few minutes later
Jesus, hearing a noise behind him,
turned and saw what was happening.

Sensing their faith, he said to
the man sick with palsy,

Son, thy sins be forgiven thee.
. . . Arise, and take up thy bed,
and go thy way into thine house.

Mark 2:5, 11

The man was immediately
healed and he gratefully embraced
his friends.

But there were certain of the
scribes, or Jewish leaders, sitting
in the crowds. Seeing what had
happened, they became jealous
and angry.

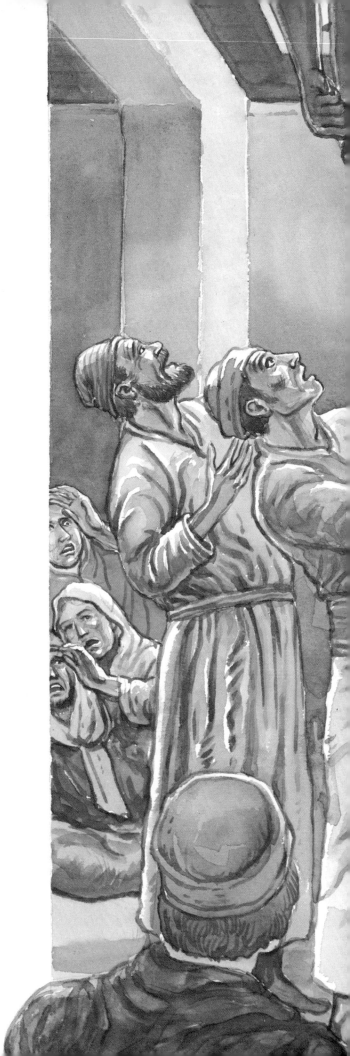

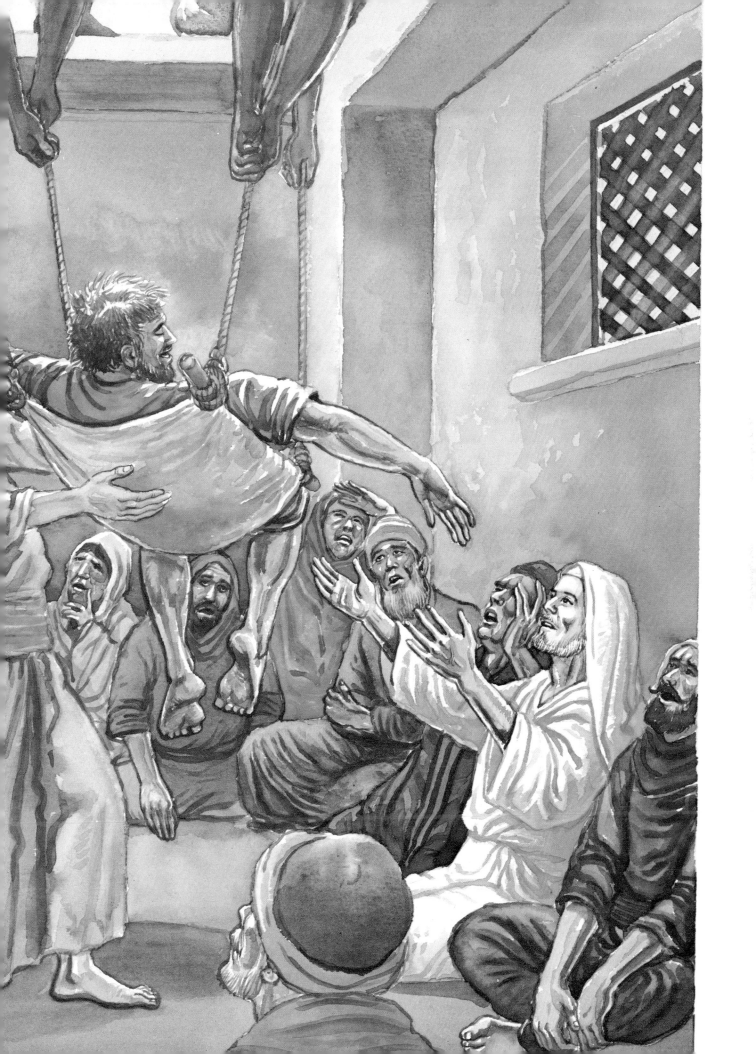

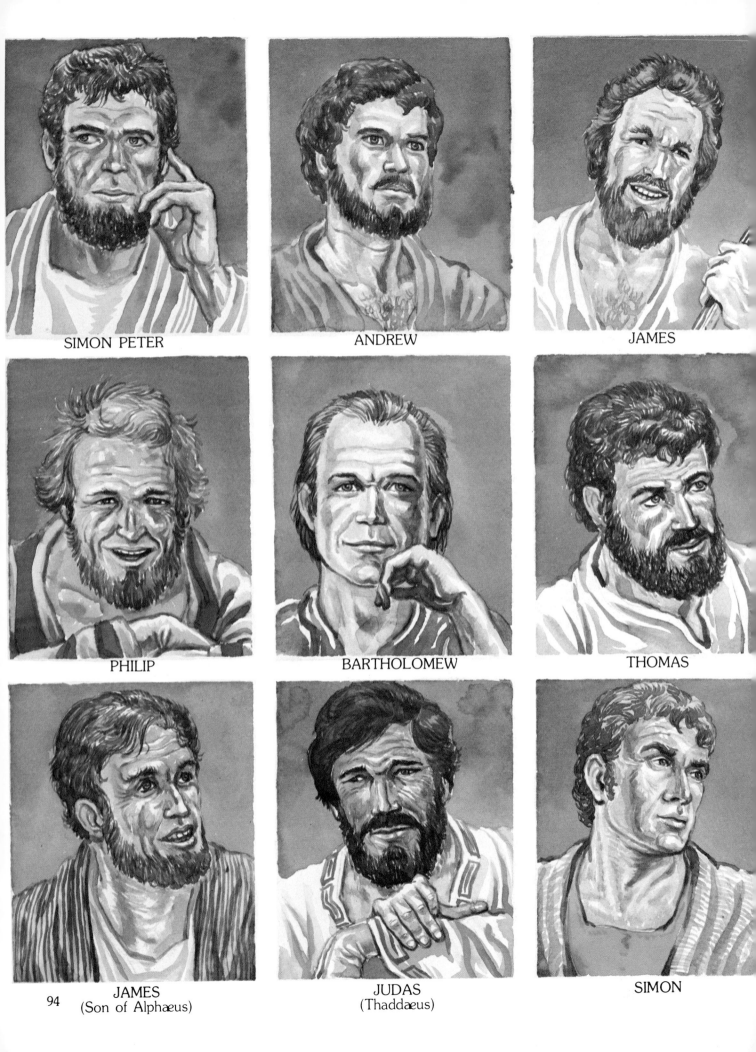

SIMON PETER

ANDREW

JAMES

PHILIP

BARTHOLOMEW

THOMAS

JAMES
(Son of Alphæus)

JUDAS
(Thaddæus)

SIMON

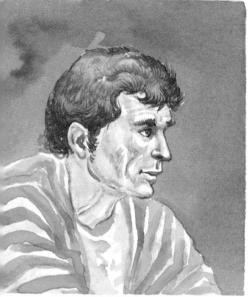

JOHN

MATTHEW

JUDAS ISCARIOT

PREPARING FOR THE FUTURE
Calling and Training the Twelve

Though there was trouble ahead for Jesus, his mission was not yet over. Having taught his disciples much by word and example, yet there was still much to do to prepare twelve men to carry on after his death.

One night, having walked into a mountain to pray, he prayed all night. When it was day, he called twelve of his disciples to him and explained that they would now become apostles or special witnesses to the world and testify that Jesus was the Christ, the Son of God. The men whom he called were named:

Simon, (whom he also named Peter,) and Andrew his brother, James and John, Philip and Bartholomew,
Matthew and Thomas, James the *son* of Alphæus, and Simon called Zelotes,
And Judas *the brother* of James, and Judas Iscariot. . . .

Luke 6:14-16

These twelve men were always near to Jesus and, as they walked along the dusty roads, he constantly taught them. In many respects they were no different from other men. They were fishermen, tax collectors, or of some other profession. Although they were not trained as leaders, they believed in Jesus and they learned from him. When they were with him, they felt confident in their faith. Jesus loved these men and prayed for them often.

These Twelve Apostles knew of Abraham, Isaac, and Jacob. They had often heard how the Israelites were given the Holy Land by the Lord. They knew that, as Jews, they were of the tribes of Israel—the chosen people. In their hearts they knew that Jesus was their Savior, but they didn't yet understand he was the Saviour for the whole world. They began realizing this fact when one day a kind and generous centurion (a Roman Captain who had command over one hundred men) sent some Jewish people to beg Jesus to come and heal his faithful servant. Those who came to Jesus had great respect for this Roman army officer because he treated the Jewish people well and had even built them a synagogue. Hearing of the goodness of this Roman, Jesus went with them. As they came near the house, the centurion saw them coming and said, "Quickly, go and tell Jesus to come no closer, for I am not worthy that he should come into my house."

The friends of the centurion gave the message to Jesus and added, "He also told us to tell you that he doesn't feel worthy to come to you either. He asks that you just say a prayer to heal his servant."

"He told us to explain to you that he is a man who has authority to say to a soldier, 'Go, and he goeth; and to another, Come, and he cometh;' and he can say to his servant, 'Do this, and he doeth it.' He knows that whatever you command will be done."

When Jesus heard these things, he marvelled at him, and turned him about, and said unto the people that followed him, I say unto you, I have not found so great faith, no, not in Israel.

And they that were sent, returning to the house, found the servant whole that had been sick.

Luke 7:9, 10

The Twelve and others now saw that Jesus was not for the Jewish people alone, but was also for this faithful Roman, as well as for all good people everywhere and throughout all time.

Soon the Twelve Apostles would be called upon to repeat what they had heard Jesus say and do.

They would continue to teach as Jesus had done, but to all peoples in every land. They would teach that Jesus was indeed the promised Messiah, the person that all the great prophets had prophesied would come.

GO IN PEACE
Faith Makes a Sick Woman Whole

In order for a miracle to occur, faith is required of the person desiring the miracle. In one instance a woman brought about a miracle without Jesus even knowing of it beforehand.

This woman had been ill for twelve years and had spent much money on doctors, who had tried to cure her but had all failed. As Jesus walked through a crowd one day, this faithful woman tried to get close to him but couldn't get through the crowd.

"Please, let me get by," she said to those between her and Jesus. Although some didn't respond, others did and soon she was only a few steps behind the Saviour. "If I can just touch his clothes," she thought, "then I know I will be healed." As she touched the border of his garment, immediately she could feel her body change and she knew that she was well. Twelve years she had waited, and now in an instant she was once again perfectly healthy.

And Jesus said, Who touched me? When all denied, Peter and they that were with him said, Master, the multitude throng thee and press *thee*, and sayest thou, Who touched me?

And Jesus said, Somebody hath touched me: for I perceive that virtue is gone out of me.

Luke 8:45, 46

Jesus had felt a portion of his healing power leave his body. He wanted to know who had such great faith that they had been healed just by touching him.

And when the woman saw that she was not hid, she came trembling, and falling down before him, she declared unto him before all the people for what cause she had touched him, and how she was healed immediately.

And he said unto her, Daughter, be of good comfort: thy faith hath made thee whole; go in peace.

Luke 8:47, 48

FINDING ONE'S LIFE
The Twelve Go on a Mission

During the time that they had been with Jesus, the Twelve Apostles had seen and heard many wonderful things. Days, weeks, and months were passing quickly. Now the time was soon coming when they would be sent forth on their own to serve the Savior by doing and saying what he had taught them. Jesus called his Twelve Apostles to him and gave them power to cast out unclean spirits and to heal all manner of sickness and disease. He then told them to tell the people that the kingdom of heaven was at hand and to heal the sick, cleanse the lepers, raise the dead, and cast out devils. He told them to take no money for what they did, for freely they had received and freely they should give.

As the twelve men sat in a group looking at Jesus, one apostle whispered to another, "He speaks so well and knows so much, but how will we remember what to say?" Jesus, sensing their concern, told them that as they traveled, people would ask them questions or desire to be taught. At these times Jesus said,

> For it is not ye that speak, but the Spirit of your Father which speaketh in you.
>
> Matthew 10:20

Each of the Twelve was grateful to hear this promise. One asked, "Although many love you, others hate you because of your words and because they are jealous of you. Will we also be hated?" Jesus replied,

> . . . ye shall be hated of all *men* for my name's sake: but he that endureth to the end shall be saved.
>
> Matthew 10:22

When one of the Twelve wondered if this hatred might cause some men to try to kill them, Jesus advised them not to be afraid. He said,

> . . . fear not them which kill the body, but are not able to kill the soul. . . .
>
> Matthew 10:28

Jesus made it clear that the Apostles, or any others who followed him, should never turn back just because someone hated them and tried to harm them. They should be faithful to him as long as they lived.

Later he said,

> He that findeth his life shall lose it: and he that loseth his life for my sake shall find it.
>
> Matthew 10:39

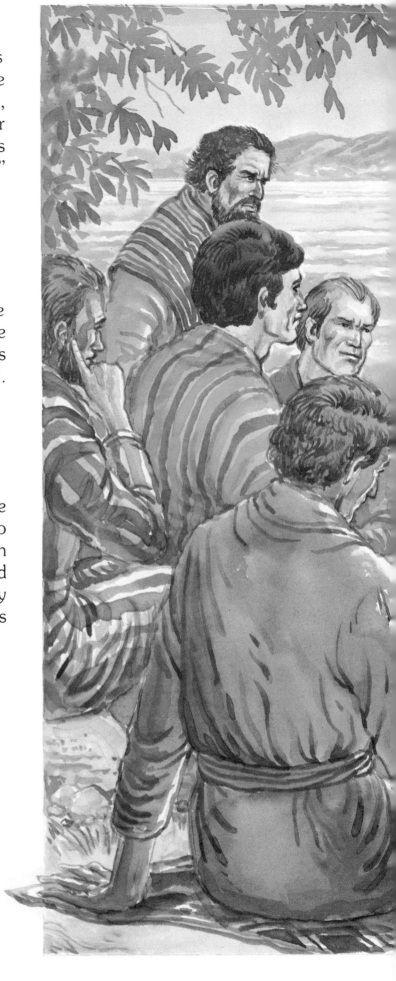

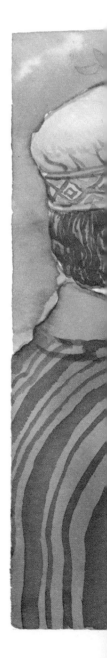

Because the Spirit of God was with the Twelve Apostles, they understood what Jesus meant. One eagerly said to his friend, "He teaches us that if we are always worried about our own lives and desires and turn away from him to find easy pleasure or comfort, we will not only lose real happiness in this life, but we will not be able to enjoy everlasting life with our Father in heaven."

Sharing his thoughts about this, his friend replied, "And if we forget ourselves in service to him and others, then we will feel joy in this life and earn an eternal life with him in heaven."

Hearing these words, Jesus was deeply pleased. His twelve students were now ready to go forth in his name. God would be with them, telling them what to say and giving them courage. They were ready to lose their lives in his service.

A short time later, after the Twelve had gone out to teach the people, Jesus stood alone. He had trained them well. Soon his life on earth would be over, but through his disciples the work he had begun could continue.

Later the Twelve returned.

And the apostles gathered themselves together unto Jesus, and told him all things, both what they had done, and what they had taught.

Mark 6:30

THINK ABOUT IT

1. Do you know someone who has found his or her life by losing it? How have they done it?
2. How can you lose your own life and find it?

THE MOST IMPORTANT FOOD
Feeding the Five Thousand

Love was a common theme in Jesus' teaching. Near the end of his three year ministry he again spoke of it to his disciples.

A new commandment I give unto you, That ye love one another; as I have loved you, that ye also love one another.

By this shall all *men* know that ye are my disciples, if ye have love one to another.

John 13:34, 35

The disciples knew that Jesus loved them, not only because of the things he said, but even more because of what he did. Everything that Jesus did—the miracles he performed, the teachings he shared, and the comfort he gave—showed his deep love for people.

One day Jesus went up into a mountain to sit with his disciples. When Jesus saw a great crowd of people coming toward him, he said to Philip, "Whence shall we buy bread, that these may eat?" (John 6:5) Jesus knew that there would be no need to buy bread, but he wanted Philip to think over the situation.

Philip answered as best he could by saying, "I don't know what to do. Even if we could buy two hundred pennyworth of bread, it would only be enough for each of them to take a little."

Andrew (Peter's brother) heard what was being said and mentioned,

> There is a lad here, which hath five barley loaves, and two small fishes: but what are they among so many?
>
> And Jesus said, Make the men sit down. Now there was much grass in the place. So the men sat down, in number about five thousand.
>
> And Jesus took the loaves; and when he had given thanks, he distributed [the food] to the disciples, and the disciples to them that were set down. . . .
>
> John 6:9-11

When all five thousand had eaten and were filled, Jesus said to his disciples,

> Gather up the fragments that remain, that nothing be lost.
>
> Therefore they gathered *them* together, and filled twelve baskets. . . .
>
> John 6:12, 13

After witnessing this miracle of the loaves and fishes, they said, "This is of a truth that prophet that should come into the world." (John 6:14)

Jesus knew that the people had been impressed because they had all been fed, but he wanted them to realize something they hadn't thought about yet. He explained, "You must always remember not only to work for the food that you eat but to seek after that food which is spiritual and which will help you gain everlasting life." When Jesus told them he would give them the word of God which he had received from his Father, they asked him,

What shall we do, that we might work the works of God?
Jesus answered and said unto them, . . . believe on him whom he hath sent.
. . . I am the bread of life: he that cometh to me shall never hunger; and he that believeth on me shall never thirst.

John 6:28, 29, 35

Some did not understand what Jesus was teaching them. They only wanted food for their bodies, not for their spirits. They told Jesus they wouldn't follow him if he didn't feed them. Turning their backs on him, they went to their homes:

> From that *time* many of his disciples went back, and walked no more with him.
> Then said Jesus unto the twelve, Will ye also go away?
> Then Simon Peter answered him, Lord, to whom shall we go? thou hast the words of eternal life.
> And we believe and are sure that thou art that Christ, the Son of the living God.

> John 6:66-69

THINK ABOUT IT

Why do people today turn away from Jesus?

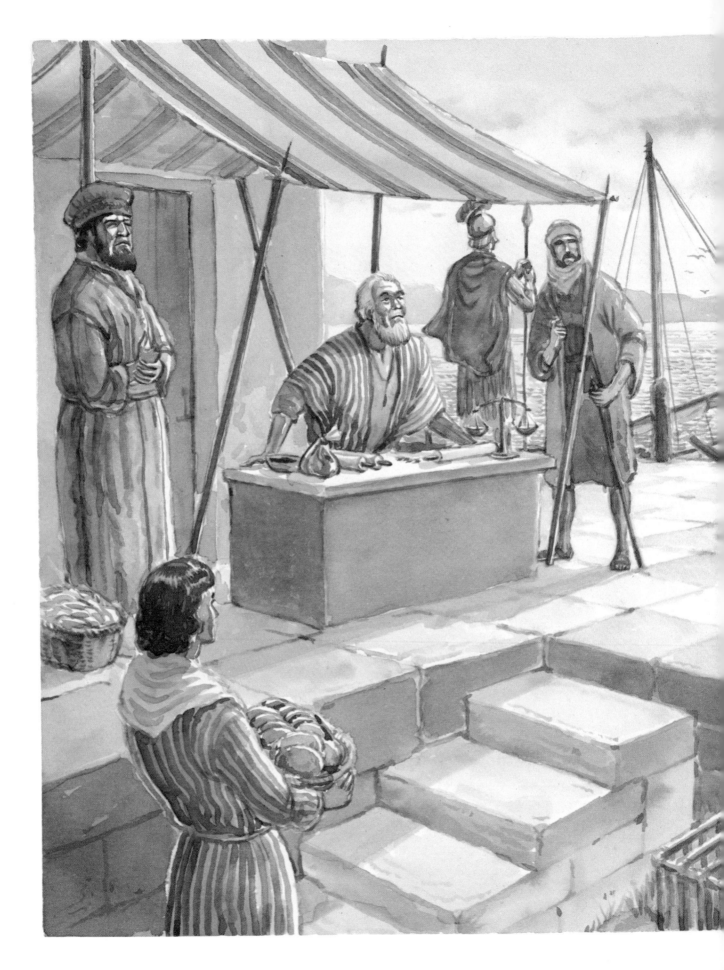

GO AND SIN NO MORE
Jesus Helps Sinners

God sent his Son, Jesus Christ, to earth to help all people change their lives by following his teachings and forsaking their sins. An unpopular group of men was known as the "publicans." These men were Jews, but they were tax collectors for the Roman government. One of them was a man named Matthew.

One day Jesus watched Matthew as the tax collector went about his work. Jesus went closer and called Matthew by his Jewish name, saying, "Levi, follow me." Levi, looking up at Jesus, immediately arose, left his work, and followed Jesus.

There was only one group of men that Jesus despised. This group consisted of Jewish leaders called scribes and Pharisees. These men felt that only they were good, and that all others should try to be like them. Jesus often spoke harshly to them:

> Woe unto you, scribes and Pharisees, hypocrites! for ye are like unto whited sepulchres, which indeed appear beautiful outward, but are within full of dead *men's* bones, and of all uncleanness.
>
> Matthew 23:27

The scribes and Pharisees did not like being called hypocrites because they knew the word hypocrite meant a person who pretends to be good but really is not. Jesus was telling these men that they were like a building that had white paint on the walls but inside was decayed and rotten. These men acted good in public, but in their hearts they were evil men. Jesus was telling the people the truth about the scribes and priests, and these leaders did not like it.

Jesus respected sinners who were willing to change and follow him, but he despised the acts of hypocrites who pretended to be good but in their hearts were disciples of Satan. It was through these wicked leaders that Satan was continually trying to destroy Jesus because he knew that Jesus had come to save the world and bring men again to peace and joy.

It would have made Jesus happy if the scribes and Pharisees had wanted to change, to stop being hypocrites, and to live the spirit of the Jewish law. He wanted all people who had committed great sins to change.

Those who heard Jesus say, "Thy sins are forgiven; go and sin no more," knew their future was in their own hands, just as ours is in our own hands today. To them and to us the love and message of Jesus is the same: "Thy faith hath saved thee. Go in peace and sin no more."

THINK ABOUT IT

If Jesus forgives us of our sins, what is our responsibility according to Jesus' words, "Go and sin no more"?

HELPING US UNDERSTAND
Teaching Through Parables

When Jesus walked along the shores of the Sea of Galilee, he would watch the fishermen mend their nets. As he walked across the flat lands some miles away, he would pause and gaze at the men casting their seeds in a wide pattern on the newly plowed earth.

He loved to sit in the hills and watch shepherds pass by with their sheep. Studying all these things, he could see they had much in common with the ideas he wanted to teach. When it was time to teach, he would tell stories that the people could understand—stories of sheep and shepherds, rich men and poor men, fish and nets, wheat and tares. He used simple, everyday occurances to teach eternal principles to the people.

Jesus' stories were short, clear, and to the point. Yet almost all of them had deep meaning that could only be found through much thought and prayer. Jesus liked to make the people search and think. He knew that the Holy Spirit was there to help them understand when they sincerely and prayerfully sought after the true meaning of his words. Thus, it was only those who loved Jesus and God with all their hearts who really understood his teachings.

NOURISH THE GOOD SEEDS
The Parable of the Sower

One day when many people were gathered around Jesus, he told them a parable.

He began: "A sower went out to sow (plant) his seeds. Reaching into a bag that was strapped to his waist, he pulled out a handful of seeds. With a sweeping motion in his arm, he threw the seeds in an even pattern upon the ground. Up and down the rows he went, continually repeating this process. As he sowed, some seeds went a little too far and fell by the wayside (the ground next to the path). Here the small plants tried to grow, but, as people and animals passed by, many of the plants were stepped on. Some of the seeds remained on top of the hard ground until they were discovered and devoured by the birds."

"Some of the seeds fell on rocky ground. The young plants sprouted, but they soon withered away and died because there was no moisture to keep them alive.

"Some of the seeds fell among thorns and weeds. They grew well here, but the weeds soon crowded them out.

"Many seeds fell on good ground, sprouted, and grew. Because their roots could go deep into the loose soil, they could receive moisture. Also, the birds could not get them, for the seeds were covered with soil. After growing to maturity, each plant produced at least 100 more kernels."

After telling this story, Jesus said, "He that hath ears to hear, let him hear." (Luke 8:8)

Feeling a little confused, some of his listeners asked to know its meaning. Jesus explained it to them carefully.

"The seed is the word (teachings) of God."

"Those seeds that were cast on the hard ground by the wayside fell among people whose hearts are hard. These people hear the teachings, but the devil, who is represented by the birds, takes the word out of their hearts. Therefore they don't believe the word and can't be saved.

"The seeds that fell on the rocks represent those that fall among people who at first receive the word with joy, but they don't let it take root in their hearts. When temptations come to them, or when people make fun of them for believing, these people fall away, just as the young plants that didn't get moisture died."

"Those seeds which fell among thorns are the ones that fall among people who, after hearing the word, go forth and are choked with the cares, riches, and pleasures of this life. They easily forget the word and do not live the way God has taught them.

"Those seeds that fell on good ground are those that fall among people who truly believe the word with all their hearts. These men, women, and children, having heard the word, keep it and bring forth the fruit of their good lives with patience."

THINK ABOUT IT:

1. If you had to tell someone what a parable was, what would you tell them?
2. How can we find the true meaning to each of the parables of Jesus?

THE HOLY LAND IN THE TIME OF CHRIST

SCALE: 20 MILES PER INCH

NABATAEANS

5 10   20   40

MEDITERRANEAN
SEA

Mt. Lebanon

SYRIA

Abila

Sidon

Damascus

PHOENICIA

MT.
HERMON

Zarephath

Leontes R.

PANIAS

Tyre

DAN

Caesarea
Philippi

ULATHA

Kedesh

L.
Semechonitis

BASHAN

Gishala

Seleucia

GALILEE

Chorazin

Raphana

Ptolemais
(Accho)

Tabigha

Bethsaida
Capernaum

GAULINITIS

Jotapata

Magdala

Cana

Tiberias

Gergesa

Gamala

SEA
OF
GALILEE

Hippos

MT.
CARMEL

Sepphoris

MT. TABOR

Yarmuk R.

Abila

Edrei

Dora

Nazareth

Nain

Capitolias

Plain of Esdraelon

Caesaria

En-gannim

Scythopolis

Bethabara

DECAPOLIS

SAMARIA

SAMARIA

Plain of Sharon

Shechem

MT. EBAL

Sychar

Apollonia

MT. GERIZIM

Jacob's Well

Jordan R.

Amathus

Jabbok R.

Antipatris

Phasaelis

Joppa

Archelais

PERAEA

AMMON

Arimathea

Ephraim

Lydda

Bethel

Jericho

Philadelphia
(Rabbath-ammon)

Gezer

Ramah

Bethany
Beyond Jordan

Jamnia

Jerusalem

Julias

Heshbon

Ekron

Emmaus

Qumran

Azotus
(Ashdod)

Bethphage

Bethany

Ascalon

Bethlehem

ARABIA

Herodium

Callirhoe

Mareshah

Machaerus

DEAD
SEA

Dibon

Hebron

En-Gedi

Arnon R.

JUDAEA

Ziph

Gaza

Juttah

Masada

Camel

Rabbath
Moab

Beersheba

Kir-haresheth

Zered R.

ARABIA

133

PREVIEW OF THINGS TO COME

Volume Nine is filled with more accounts of the inspiring and motivating parables of Jesus. We will want to help others more when we learn about the Good Samaritan. The story of the Prodigal Son will remind us to stay close to our families and to God. We will read of how Satan causes jealousy to come into the hearts of the Jewish leaders as the fame of Jesus grows.

An account will be given of Lazarus being raised from the tomb. We will read of Jesus riding a donkey on his triumphal entry into Jerusalem. We will learn about Jesus' Last Supper and of the great atoning sacrifice made by Jesus in the Garden of Gethsemene.

We will read of Jesus' willingness to die, making it possible for everyone to be resurrected and live again after death. The story of the crucifixion and resurrection will be related. Volume Nine will be worth remembering.